THE WIZARD WHO WANTED TO BE SANTA

DEDICATION

For my Earth Angels: Ilana Flora Wai Ying Wurman,
Chaya Rosie Wai Tao Wurman, Mikael Logan Wurman
and Farrah Leigh McDonough with all my heart. *G.N.*

For Brian, Jake and Kyle with wishes to keep
Santa in their hearts forever. *S.C.*

THE WHOW WOW TO BE

BY GLORIA NAGY

IZARD

ANTED

SANTA

DRAWINGS BY **SEYMOUR CHWAST**

SHEER BLISS
COMMUNICATIONS LLC
NEWPORT RHODE ISLAND 02840

In a land so far away that people's
Names are hard to say
There lived a wizard called Beedlebas
Who wanted to become Santa Claus.

In his castle on a fog-covered strand
Beedlebas would scheme and plan
For months and months he'd hide away
And pace the floor till Christmas Day.

And every time the day had passed,
He'd rant and rave and talk so fast,
"Unfair," he'd cry, "Unfair to me!
Santa Claus is all they see!
The children never get to test
If Santa really is the best."

Year after year he carried on
After Christmas was long since gone
Mean and old and ugly as a crow
He'd whine and wail and holler so
That soon his voice would fade away
And he'd just mope till next Christmas Day.

And then one Christmas a thought appeared
That lifted his spirit and twittered his beard
And scratching and thinking he made his way
Out of his castle and far astray.

"I've got it! Hee Hee! The solution is clear!
I'll hold an election, the children will hear!
A democracy we have they say,
Well, I'll beat Santa the American way!
An election it is! What fun it will be!
Just old tubby Santa, the children and Me!"

"Oops!" said Beedlebas,
"I can't go out there!
My clothes are a mess
And just look at my hair!
It's a new look I need
To make the brats swoon.

I could be an astronaut
And fly to the moon
Or a football hero or
A motorcycle whiz.
I must find the right image
To capture the kids . . . ??
A rocker I'll be
With music and wigs!"

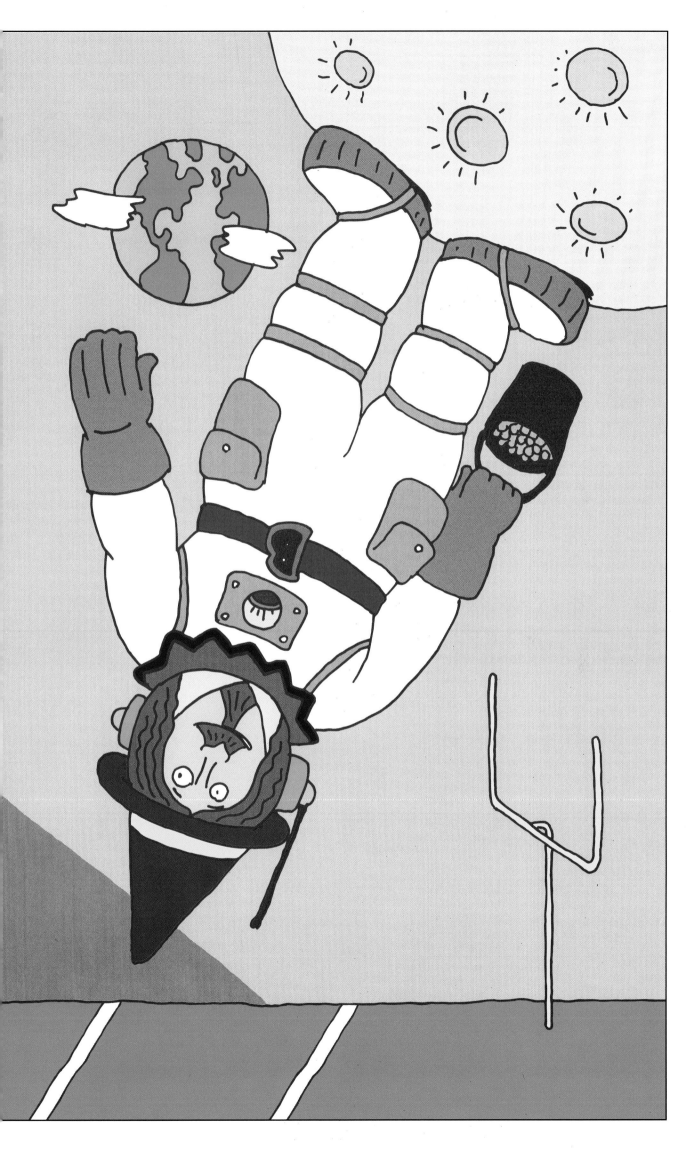

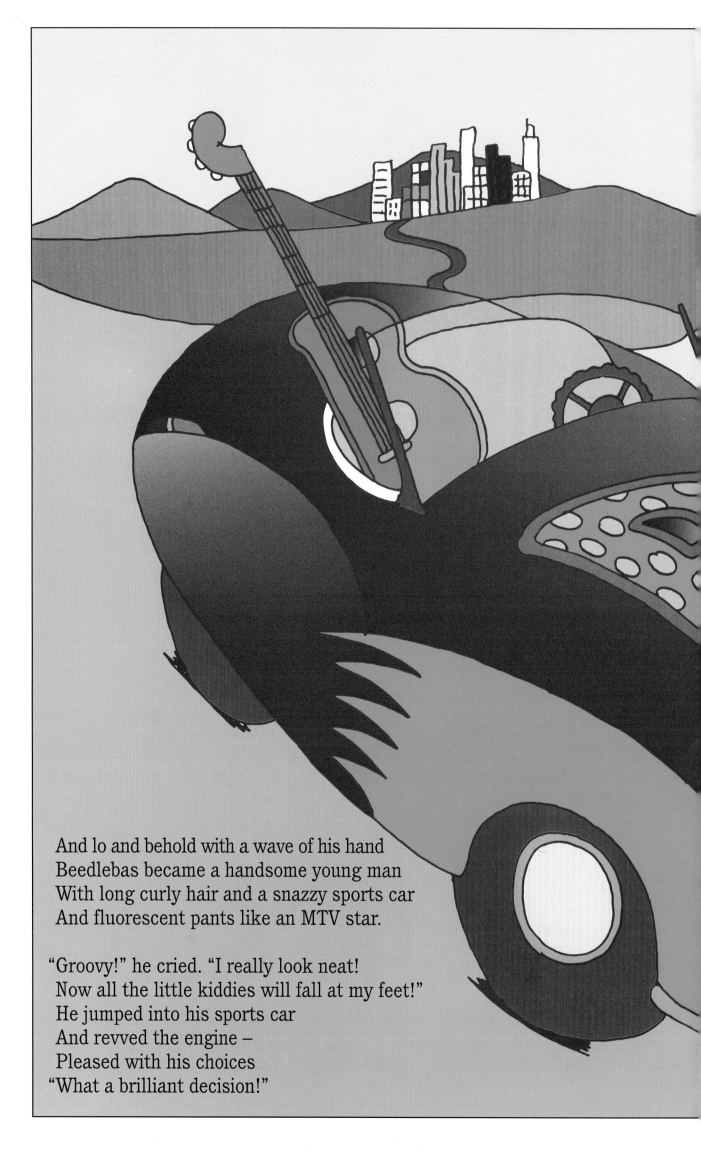

And lo and behold with a wave of his hand
Beedlebas became a handsome young man
With long curly hair and a snazzy sports car
And fluorescent pants like an MTV star.

"Groovy!" he cried. "I really look neat!
Now all the little kiddies will fall at my feet!"
He jumped into his sports car
And revved the engine –
Pleased with his choices
"What a brilliant decision!"

So cackling and honking the old Wizard raced
Across mountains and deserts as if he were chased
And reaching the Metropolis he paused at the door
Of the famous department store Muffin & More.

Now Muffin & More is where Santa resided
When he was in town and his gifts undecided
And singing and humming the latest hit song
He knew that Santa would soon be gone.

The very next day at Muffin & More
Jolly old Santa was walking the floor
A tear in his eye had rolled down his cheek
And kindly old Santa was too sad to speak.

My children, my children, he thought to himself,
Are turning from Santa to somebody else.
A handsome young fellow with yellow tight pants
Strong enough to sing and wiggle and dance!
An election will be held, they say, very soon
And the children will vote on how well we can croon!
Oh woe is me, I'm not a hip cat,
My belly is round – and my voice is quite flat.

Poor old Santa was quite in despair –
He even considered dyeing his hair
When tired at last he went to his bed
And fell fast asleep with his cap on his head.

And during the night Santa did dream
And Erak his helper appeared on the scene.
"Santa," he whispered, "So sweet and so dear,
Just be who you are and the children will hear
A voice like an angel as good as your heart.
The children will know – children are smart."

When Santa awoke he remembered the dream
And how much brighter the world did seem!
"Ho, Ho!" he chuckled, "Ho, Ho, Ho, Ho!
It looks like Santa is still in the show!"

On the day before Christmas at Muffin & More
Thousands of children pushed through the door
The announcer came out and said very grand
That the children would vote by raising their hand.

"We want Beedlebas!" They yelled and they screamed
And the Wizard appeared all polished and gleamed
He opened his mouth and started to sing
He wiggled and shook and said he was king.

Beedlebas Blues

Come near all you kiddies
It's time to choose
We'll be singin'
We'll be swingin'
We'll be spreadin' the news!

We'll be movin'
We'll be groovin'
To the Beedlebas Blues
The Beedlebas Blues
We'll be rockin' in our shoes!

Vote for me!
I'm the King
I'm the coolest of cool
I'm the handsomest thing!

No more preachers
No more teachers

No more homework
No more school
No more parents to obey –
You can watch TV all day!

No more spinach to eat
No more rooms to keep neat
You'll eat junk food galore
I'll buy out every store!

Don't brush your teeth
Don't comb your hair
and if you want to dress funny
there's nothin' you can't wear!

Don't feed the cat
Don't tie your shoes
And if you like acting goofy
You got nothin' to lose!

Vote for me! I'm the King
I'm so cool
I'm the grooviest thing
Vote for me...Vote for me! I'm the King!

The children all clapped and leapt to their feet,
"He's groovy, he's great, he's really a treat!"
Beedlebas bowed and smug as could be
Swaggered away to wait and to see.

Erak was nervous and Santa was, too.
They waited for the announcer to give them their cue.
"Well little friend, it seems he's a star.
This may be the last time our sleigh goes this far."
Erak hugged Santa as hard as he could.
"Never fear Santa, the children are good."

Then out came old Santa as plump as a plum
His cheeks all rosy and he began to hum
He hummed a lullaby in his flat creaky style
And all of the children began to smile
And pretty soon they were all sound asleep
Dreaming of snowmen and good things to eat.

Santa's Hymn

When you grow very tall
Don't forget you know it all
La La La ... Li Li Li
Children solve the mystery
La La La ... Li Li Li
Children hold our history

Children know
Children feel
What is false and what is real
Children know
Children hear
What to love and what to fear

In their cribs
In their beds
In their hearts and in their heads

Who is nice
Who is mean
Who is somewhere in between

Children know
Children see
Who they are and what to be
La La La ... Li Li Li

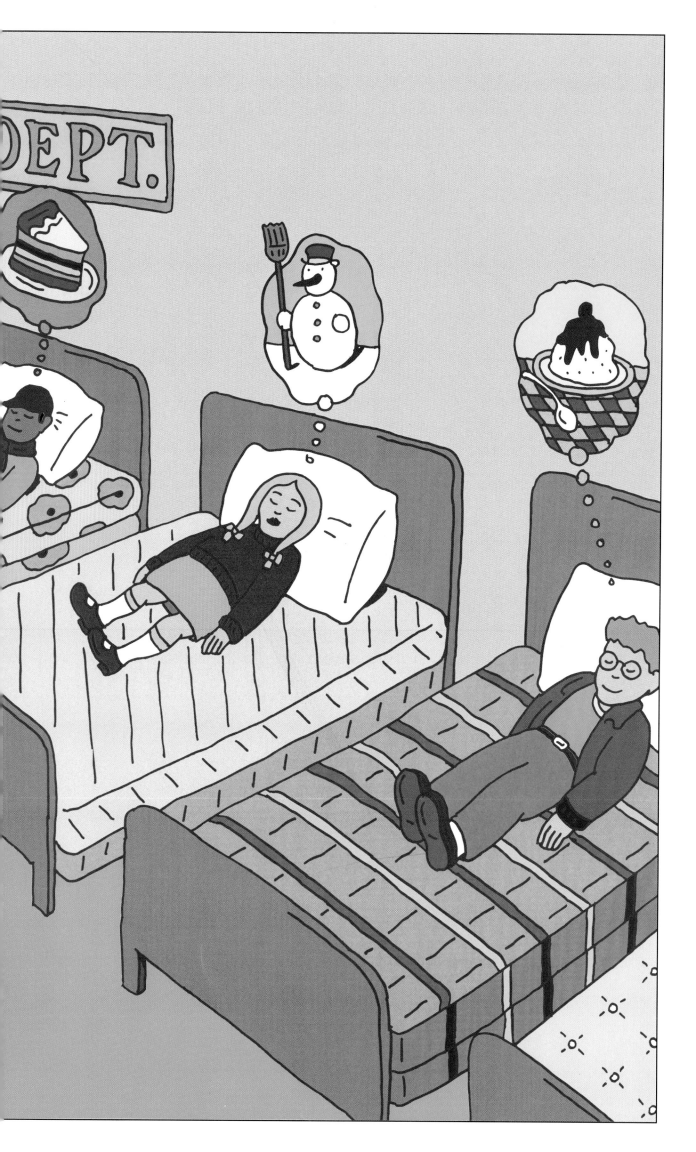

"But the vote!" cried Beedlebas
   All in a rage,
"Shake them awake,
   Get them up on the stage!"

The children were snoring
And sleeping so sound
When the floor beneath them
Began to pound,
And the ceiling above them
Started to quiver
And the furious Wizard
Began to shiver.

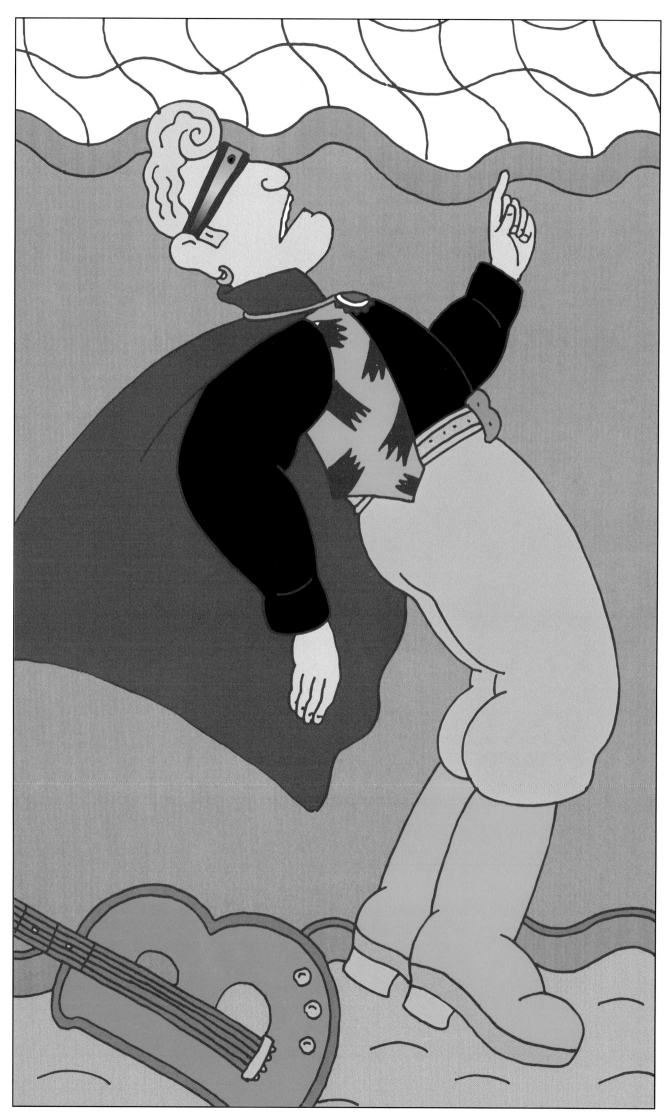

"An earthquake! An earthquake!" Santa said in alarm,
"I must help the children and keep them from harm!"
Dolls and teddy bears flew through the air,
The children awoke with wind in their hair.

"Save us, Beedlebas!" they hollered and cried,
"We need your power to help us survive!"
They ran toward the Wizard as the walls were falling
But Beedlebas was so frightened he started howling.

Erak leapt forward too angry to leave
"You must help the children –
They can't be deceived!"

"Get out of my way! Don't whimper and moan!
 I just want to beat Santa and sit on his throne!"
 Then miracle of miracles, Santa swept down in his sleigh
 And gathered the children  and whisked them away.

Beedlebas grabbed Erak and jumped into his seat,
"You're mine now, you baby – Santa's final defeat!"

"He's got Erak!" yelled the children
 As Beedlebas zoomed past –
"He's headed for a snowbank
 And he's going too fast!"

The children shrieked and Beedlebas crashed
Flipping and sliding – his car was all smashed.
Santa touched down though the children were wary
They had all seen the Wizard cowardly and scary.
"Santa, where's Erak? Is he okay?
We all saw Beedlebas take him away!"

Beedlebas popped up struggling out of the rubble
Steaming and stewing and looking for trouble.
"I know what you did! You think I'm a dope?
You started the quake to call off the vote!"

And while he spoke,
An aftershock started
And the ice beneath him
Suddenly parted!
"Save me!" sobbed Beedlebas,
Grabbing at the sleigh.
"Up, up!" he screeched,
"Up and away!"

Erak woke up with a lump on his head
"Let go!" he shouted, "or we'll all be dead!"
He ran like a reindeer, knocking Beedlebas down,
And rolled him away from the crack in the ground.

Beedlebas pushed Erak out of his way,
"We must have the election, this is the day!"
He slicked back his hair, he grimaced and grinned,
"You kiddies remember what you get if I win!"

Santa just sighed and climbed out of his sleigh
And Beedlebas joined him, wanting his way.
"But that's why we came back," said Santa with pride,
"The children must choose, I've nothing to hide."

Then Erak crawled out
From under the snow.
He had to help Santa –
The children must know!
"Remember the lullaby,
You know what is true.
Just trust in yourselves
And you'll know what to do."

"Santa's our hero!" the children proclaimed,
"Santa forever, our vote stays the same!"

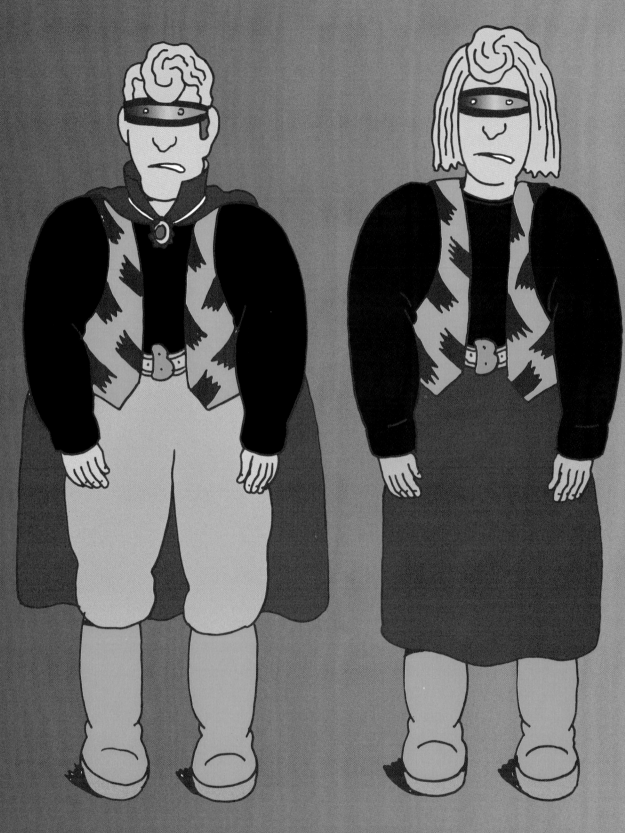

The Wizard he screamed
And raved on so

That his magic gave out
And he started to crow

And all of his handsomeness
Melted away

And he never returned
To this very day.

ACKNOWLEDGMENTS

Deepest thanks to Seymour for his magic hand
and for making me work harder; Joe Smith for being
a wonderful pal, collaborator and composer and
Richard Saul Wurman for making my dream come true.